# SNIP AND THE DRAGON'S SKIN

Snip was a fisherman, and he lived by the sea. When the sun shone, and the sky was blue, Snip went out fishing in his boat.

But Snip was not a very good fisherman, and things didn't go very well.

One day, when he was pulling in his nets, he slipped, and fell into the sea. He pulled himself out, but he lost all his fish.

The next day, the sun shone, and the sky was blue. The sea was as blue as the sky. There was no wind. So Snip set out to sea. He sailed out a long, long way, before he set the nets.

He sailed out too far. The sun set. Snip could not find his nets in the dark, and when the sun came up the next day, the nets were gone.

It took him a long, long time to make some more.

One day, just as Snip was going down to his boat, an old fisherman stopped him.

"Don't go out fishing today, Snip," said the old man. "Look at the sky. There is a storm coming."

"The sun is shining," said Snip. "I am going fishing."

And he went.

That was the day that Snip lost his boat.

He was just setting his nets, when the wind began to blow.

The wind blew harder and harder.

The nets broke away in the storm, and were lost in the sea.

The sails blew away in the wind.

The boat was blown on to the rocks.

The waves tossed Snip up on the rocks, and he pulled himself out of the sea.

But the boat broke up, as the big waves crashed over it.

Then Snip had no fish, and no nets, and no boat.

So Snip went out fishing with another fisherman, called Sam.

"But it is a bit hard," Snip said to himself.

"Why should I have to help Sam? Yes, it is a bit hard!"

Snip wasn't happy, and things didn't go very well.

The first day, when Snip was helping Sam to set the sails, Snip let go of his rope too soon.

The sail fell on Sam's head with a crash!

The second day, the sun shone, and the
sky was blue. Sam took Snip out fishing.

Sam was on one side of the boat, and
Snip was on the other.

It was very hot in the sunshine. Snip
went to sleep.

A very big fish got into the nets on Snip's side of the boat. Snip was sleeping in the sunshine.

The fish was too big for the net. He broke away from the net, and let all the other fish out too.

Snip woke up to find the fish all gone.

"It is a bit hard," Snip said to himself. "Yes, it is a bit hard. Why did that fish come to *my* side of the boat?"

The very next day, when Sam was climbing down into the boat, Snip went to give him a hand.

Sam didn't want a hand. But just as he got to Sam, Snip slipped and fell. He fell into Sam, and Sam fell right into the sea.

Snip tossed Sam a rope, and then, just as
Sam was pulling himself back into the boat,
Snip let the rope go, and Sam fell back into
the sea.

When Sam climbed back into his boat,
he was very wet, and he was very cross.
  "This is the last time you sail with me!"
he said.

The other fishermen would not have Snip in their boats, so Snip had nothing to do. He had no boat, and he could not go fishing. But he had to eat. So he went up and down on the sands, looking for shell-fish. He ate the fish, and he sold the shells.

"But it is a bit hard," Snip said to himself. "I have lost my nets and I have lost my boat, and no one will help me. Yes, it is a bit hard, it is indeed."

Snip went off to live in a cave by the sea.
One day, he was on the sands looking for shell-fish. He had gone a long way, when he saw something green on the rocks ahead. It was a very big green something.

Snip hid behind a rock.

"It looks like a dragon," he said to himself.

But the green something lay still.

Snip went a little nearer.

"It *is* a dragon," he said.

But still the dragon did not move.

"Perhaps the dragon is asleep," said Snip.

He went a little nearer.

Then he saw that it was not a dragon at all. It was a dragon's skin.

Every ten years, a green dragon grows a new skin. This was the old skin of a green dragon.

Snip looked at the skin for a long time.
Then he laughed. "I know what I shall
do," he said. "No one would let me go out
in a boat. No one would let me help with
the fishing. But they are all afraid of dragons.
I know what I shall do now!"

Snip hid the dragon's skin among the rocks till the sun had set. Then, as the moon came up over the hills, he took the dragon's skin back to his cave.

He had to pull the skin along on the sands, but he got it back in the end.

The moon shone down. The sands were white in the moonlight.

Snip set the dragon skin on the sands near his cave. He filled it full of sand and stones. From a little way away, the skin looked just like a real dragon, asleep on the sands.

As soon as the sun came up, Snip was out looking for fishing boats.

There were some rocks near his cave, running out into the sea. Snip climbed out over the rocks. He sat down at the end of the rocks in the sunshine.

He didn't go to sleep this time.

There was good fishing off the end of the
rocks, and it was not long before a fishing
boat came by.

Snip stood up, and put his hands to his
mouth.

"Ho, there!" he called.

"What is it?" the fishermen called back.

"Do you see that dragon asleep on the
sands?" cried Snip. "He is my dragon. He
lives in my cave. Give me all your fish, or I
will send my dragon to take it!"

The fishermen were frightened.

The dragon looked very big.

They gave Snip all the fish they had, and sailed away as fast as they could.

Snip stood on the rocks looking after them.

"That's one in the eye for you!" he said to himself. "Yes, that's one in the eye for you!"

He picked up the fish, and took it back over the rocks to his cave.

The next day, another fishing boat came by.

Snip was out at the end of the rocks.

"Give me some food," he cried. "Give me all the food you have, or I will set my dragon on you!"

The fishermen were frightened when they saw the dragon. They gave Snip all their food, and sailed away as fast as they could.

The very next day, the Black Pirates sailed by the rocks, in a big ship with black sails.

Snip was a bit frightened when he saw the Black Pirates.

But he called out to them: "Give me a sack of gold! Give me a sack of gold, Black Pirates, or I shall set my dragon on you!"

Even the Black Pirates were afraid of dragons, and this dragon looked very big.

They gave Snip a sack of gold, and sailed away as fast as they could.

But when they had sailed a little way, the
Black Pirates began to think about Snip
and his dragon. They thought it was very
strange that a man like Snip should have a
real dragon with him.

So they sailed across to the island where
the Sea-Witch lived, to tell the Sea-Witch
about it.

They found the Sea-Witch by her fire on the sand, and they told her what had happened.

The Sea-Witch laughed her black laugh.

"I must go and see Snip and his dragon," she said.

When Snip came out of his cave the next morning, he saw Sam's boat out to sea.

Sam was fishing.

Snip climbed out to the end of the rocks.

"Sam!" he called out. "Sam! You must give me that boat. Bring it in on the sands by my cave, or I shall set my dragon on you!"

Sam hardly looked at him.

"If you want my boat, you must come and take it!" he called back over the water. "I'll fight you, Snip, and I'll fight your dragon, if you lay a hand on my boat!"

Snip didn't know what to do. He turned and went slowly back over the rocks towards his cave.

But when he got back to the sands, he saw the Sea-Witch standing at the mouth of the cave.

She saw Snip coming, and she laughed her black laugh.

"So you have found one sailor who is not frightened of a dragon's skin, have you Snip?" she said. "And what do you think the Black Pirates will do to you, when I tell them that your dragon is just an old skin?"

"Oh, don't do that!" cried Snip. "Don't tell the Black Pirates! You must help me, Sea-Witch."

"Why should I?" asked the Sea-Witch.

"Because if you will help me, I will give you a sack of gold," said Snip.

"And where did *you* get a sack of gold?" asked the Sea-Witch.

"The Black Pirates gave it to me," said Snip. "But you shall have it, Sea-Witch, if you will help me."

The Sea-Witch stood and looked at Snip for a long time.

Snip did not feel at all happy. He stood first on one foot, and then on the other.

"What do you want me to do?" asked the Sea-Witch at last.

"Send me a dragon, a real dragon," said Snip. "Then, if anyone won't give me all I ask for, I can send a real dragon after him."

"So you want a real dragon, do you?" said the Sea-Witch.

"Yes," said Snip. "Send me a real dragon, and you can have the sack of gold."

The Sea-Witch looked out over the sea.
Then she looked at the dragon's skin.
Then she looked at Snip, and she laughed.
Snip didn't like the laugh very much. It
made him feel frightened.

"Very well," said the Sea-Witch. "You
shall have a real dragon, Snip. Where is the
Black Pirates' gold?"

"It's not the Black Pirates' gold," said
Snip. "It's my gold. The Black Pirates
gave it to me. I hid it."

"Go and get it," said the Sea-Witch.
"Put it in the mouth of your cave. I am
going now. I shall take the gold when I
come back with a dragon."

Snip went off for the sack of gold. When he came back to the cave, the Sea-Witch had gone.

He set the sack of gold down in the mouth of the cave, just as the Sea-Witch had said.

Snip didn't see the Sea-Witch again that day, but when he came out of his cave the next morning the sack of gold had gone.

He could see nothing new on the sands. The dragon skin was just where he had left it. It looked just as it had before, as if a dragon lay sleeping on the sands.

"That witch!" said Snip. "That witch! She's taken my gold and given me nothing for it! I shall know what to do, if I meet her again! I have still got nothing but an old skin!"

He picked up a rock, and tossed it at the dragon's skin as hard as he could.

The dragon lifted his head and roared.
Two big, red eyes turned towards Snip.
The dragon saw Snip standing there in
the mouth of the cave. With another roar,
he shot up into the air.

Snip was too frightened to move.
His legs shook under him.
He stood there on the sand, shaking.

Down came the dragon, his eyes flashing
red fire. In a flash, he had taken Snip in his
claws, and sailed up into the air, roaring as
he went.

The dragon shot high into the air. Higher
and higher and higher he went, up over the
sands and the rocks, and out over the sea.

Snip shut his eyes.
He was too frightened to cry out.
He was too frightened to move.
He was too frightened to think.
He just hung there in the dragon's claws,
as the dragon shot out over the sea.

On they went, on and on and on, far out over the sea.

The dragon's roars filled Snip's ears. The dragon roared, and roared again. Then, just as Snip thought that he must be dead, the dragon dropped like a stone.

The dragon dropped till he nearly touched the waves, and then he shot up into the air again. But as he shot up, he let go of Snip.

Snip fell out of the dragon's claws, and dropped like a stone into the sea.

Snip went down under the water. The sea filled his eyes and the sea filled his ears.

Then he came up again, into the sunshine.

"Help!" he cried. "Help!" as the waves broke over his head.

Snip felt himself moving. Something was pulling him along. For a second, he thought that the dragon had got hold of him again.

Then he found himself being pulled over the side of a boat. He looked up.

There was Sam, the fisherman, pulling in his fishing net, and Snip was the biggest fish in the net!

Sam pulled Snip in over the side.

Snip fell into the boat. He just lay there, with his eyes shut.

Sam turned the boat back to the island. He did what he could to help Snip, but Snip wanted to lie still. So in the end Sam just let him lie there in the boat and sailed back as fast as he could.

From that day on, Snip lived in a little hut down by the sea. Every day, he went out looking for shell-fish. He ate the fish, and he sold the shells.

"But it's a bit hard," he said to himself, as he climbed over the rocks. "It's a bit hard! No one will help me. I lost my fish and I lost my nets, I lost my boat and I lost my gold. I even lost my dragon's skin! *Anyone* would think that was a bit hard. And it *is* a bit hard, it is indeed!"